C000274310

THE TIMES
QUEEN'S COUNSEL III

THE TIMES

QUEEN'S COUNSEL III

LAYING DOWN THE LAW

BY STEUART & FRANCIS

Published by
News International plc
P.O. Box 495
Virginia Street
London E1 9XY

Copyright © Alex Steuart Williams and Graham Francis Defries, 1998

All rights reserved. No part of this book may be reproduced, stored in a retrieval system, or transmitted in any form or by any means electronic, mechanical, photocopying, recording or otherwise without the prior written permission of the publisher and copyright owner.

British Library Cataloguing in Publication Data
A catalogue record for this title is available from the British Library

Printed and bound in Great Britain by Butler and Tanner

I S B N   1 902254 12 0

The Times is a registered trademark of Times Newspapers Ltd

The Times
LONDON

Biography

Alex Steuart Williams is a former barrister turned cartoonist and feature film animator. He is currently working at Dreamworks film studios in Los Angeles on the forthcoming The Road To El Dorado. *His film credits include* Who Framed Roger Rabbit?, The Lion King *and* Pocahontas. *His cartoons have been published in* The Times *and* Tatler.

Graham Francis Defries is a solicitor with the City law firm Bird & Bird. Prior to becoming a lawyer, he had a range of jobs including a parliamentary research assistant for a Member of Parliament and a music promoter. In addition to books of Queen's Counsel cartoons, he has contributed to Internet Law and Regulation, published by FT Law & Tax. He is married with a young son and lives in London.

Acknowledgements

For Emma, Kitty and Charlie, with special thanks to David Driver whose continued help and support has made this book possible, to Mo Sutton for some invaluable suggestions, and to the lawyers at Bird & Bird for laughing at the jokes.

Foreword by Sir Geoffrey Bentwood QC

It gives me great pleasure, as one of England's leading silks, and as the chief protagonist of "Queen's Counsel", to have been invited by the authors to introduce this admirable collection of (allegedly) humorous drawings. This is not without irony, as those readers familiar with the recent proceedings of the Queen's Bench Division will no doubt be aware.

For some 5 years now I have been engaged in litigation with Messrs Steuart and Francis over their portrayal of me in this so-called "cartoon strip", in which I am held up to ridicule and regularly accused of pomposity, vanity, prolixity, and a condescending attitude towards my clients and instructing solicitors. Can one imagine a more grievous slander upon the unsullied reputation of an esteemed advocate such as myself?

I anticipate shortly being the beneficiary of substantial libel damages, and it is therefore with very real sincerity that I wish Messrs Steuart and Francis the greatest of success with their publication, that they may be better able to pay any award in full. What more compelling reason could there be for buying this book?

Sir Geoffrey Bentwood QC
4 Lawn Buildings
Temple EC4

Contents

Legal Fees

"A man may as well open an oyster without a knife, as a lawyer's mouth without a fee"

Barten Holyday

client / ˈklʌɪənt / *n.* 1 A person with money who does not wish to pay bills.

14

16

Legal Advice

"Ignorance of the law excuses no man from practicing it"

Addison Mizner

WHEN LAWYERS WIN

... AND WHEN THEY LOSE

THEORY OF RELATIVITY

WILL MY JUDGMENT BE OVERTURNED ON APPEAL IF I FIND FOR THE PLAINTIFF TODAY?

30

Lawyers at Large

*"Every once in a while you meet a
fellow in some honourable walk of
life that was once admitted to the Bar"*

Frank McKinney Hubbard

35

SPOT THE LAWYER

LAWYER'S VIDEO STORE

47

Trial and Error

"We have a criminal system which is superior to any in the world, and its efficiency is only marred by the difficulty of finding 12 men every day who don't know anything and can't read"

Mark Twain

50

52

RULES OF TV LAW
① THE PERSON ON TRIAL IS NEVER GUILTY

② THE GUILTY PERSON IS SOMEWHERE IN THE COURT

③ THE LAWYER WHOSE NAME IS IN THE TITLE OF THE PROGRAM NEVER LOSES

④ IT'S ALL MUCH MORE INTERESTING THAN THE REAL THING

AND FINALLY, M'LUD.

Z
ZZ
Z Z

57

PLEASE TELL THE COURT, IN YOUR OWN WORDS, WHAT HAPPENED ON THE NIGHT OF THE ROBBERY.
ER... CAN'T I USE MY LAWYER'S WORDS INSTEAD?

Lawyer vs Lawyer

"Lawyers earn a living by the sweat of their browbeating"

James G Huneker

THE FINANCE COMMITTEE OF PAYE, CASH & PRAYE ATTEMPT TO SETTLE UP A RESTAURANT BILL.

| HM, LET'S SEE ... CLAUSE 1(6) "ALL PARTIES SHALL ACT DILIGENTLY AND IN GOOD FAITH TO PERFORM THE TERMS HEREIN. | ... ANY DISAGREEMENT IN LAW OR EQUITY SHALL BE DECIDED BY NEUTRAL BINDING ARBITRATION. | THIS CONTRACT CONSTITUTES THE ENTIRE, FINAL AND EXCLUSIVE EXPRESSION OF THE AGREEMENT BETWEEN THE PARTIES. | OH DARLING — IT'S SO ROMANTIC DRAFTING OUR OWN PRE-NUPTIAL AGREEMENT TOGETHER. |

The Legal Ladder

"Lawyers, I suppose, were children once"

Charles Lamb

FOUR STEPS TO BECOMING A BARRISTER:
① PASS BAR FINALS.

HOW MANY LAWYERS DOES IT TAKE TO CHANGE A LIGHT BULB?
(a) 5
(b) 10
(c) HOW MANY CAN YOU AFFORD?

② DRESS WITH THE DIGNITY THAT BEFITS THE BAR

BILL £450

③ LEARN THE SECRETS OF THE LAW AT INNS OF COURT DINNERS

④ GO INTO FAMILY LAW

WELCOME TO CHAMBERS, NEPHEW

HOW LEGAL REFORM WORKS:

LEGAL OLYMPICS

SYNCHRONISED BILLING

CROSS-COUNTRY AMBULANCE DASH

PARTNERSHIP PROMOTION WRESTLE

LONG DISTANCE RUN UP EXPENSE ACCOUNT

Legal Sleaze

"God works wonders now and then.
Behold, a lawyer, an honest man"

Benjamin Franklin

LEGAL BUILDERS

EROTIC DAYDREAMS FOR TAX LAWYERS

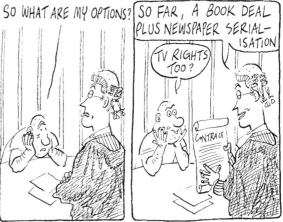

93

To order additional copies of:
The Times Queen's Counsel III Laying Down The Law
RRP £7.99 available for just £5.99

or the earlier volumes:
The Times Queen's Counsel 1: A Libellous Look at the Law
RRP £4.99 available for just £3.99
The Times Queen's Counsel 2: Judgment Day
RRP £4.99 available for just £3.99

Please call The Times Bookshop on 0990 134 459
or send your cheque/postal order to:
The Times Bookshop, PO Box 345, Falmouth, TR11 2YX
or by e-mail at "bookshop@the-times.co.uk"

All orders are subject to availability

Original cartoons featured in The Times Queen's Counsel may be purchased subject to availability.

To order please contact Graham Defries on 0171 415 6000
or by e-mail at "Graham.Defries@twobirds.com"